This book belongs to

_____

_____

_____

THE SPECIAL ONE

By Kayla N. Gorham

"You are the light of the world. A city set on a hill cannot be hidden. Your word is a lamp for my feet, a light on my path."

– Matthew 5:14

In the beginning, when Earth was yet young,
There lived a bright star, and sky-high she hung.

She sparkled, she glistened, she had a bright light,
Of all other stars, she was greatest in sight.

**Best friends with the clouds, great times they did share,
They played funny games, even musical chairs.**

But time had gone by, and the star was so shy,
Behind the great billows of clouds, she did hide.

Most stars were so small, but she was so big,
She felt they were laughing, so she often hid.

But they were not laughing, they liked her so much,
The other stars knew she was special and such.

Of all the kind stars, that wished to be friends
The brightest of all said, "I WISH TO FIT IN!"

But as time went on, the air became warm,
The friendly clouds knew it was time for a storm.

The clouds were her friends, but had to move on,
The star could not hide behind billows for long.

"I wish to be hidden", the star simply said.
"It's great to be different!", the friendly clouds pled...

"Your light is so special, so do not be shy."
Plants need your bright light, or surely, they'll die."

BOOM! BANG! The thunder was loud,
"You have to believe you are great!", cried the clouds

The star was afraid, but she shined her light,
The storm was now over, no clouds were in sight.

And plants were so happy on Earth down below,
"They've watered and fed us and now we can grow!"

And then the wind blew, the clouds were not far,
So now they were back to play games with the star.

So, in the beginning, when Earth was yet young,
The star was afraid to outshine everyone.

But many years later, she sparkles for fun,
She's glad to be different, for she is the sun.

Color the Earth.

Color the Sun.

Color the Rainbow.

Made in the USA
Columbia, SC
15 May 2023

16710763R00015